Contents

Fire at the Museum

Diana, Narrator, Noel

Narrator

Noel looked out of the window at the flashing neon light over the video store. Diana would be home soon.

Noel

Should I go and get a video or play my violin while I wait for Diana?

Narrator

Just then Noel heard shouts, then a siren, and Diana and a stranger rushed through the door.

Noel

What is it? What's going on?

Diana

It's a fire at the museum! It's chaotic out there!

Noel

What happened?

Diana

The string duet was playing a minuet from the show *Romeo and Juliet* that's just opened in town. Before that, Violet read the poem *Triumph* from her new collection of poetry called *Cameo*.

Noel
So where did all
this happen?

Diana
The performance was
inside the museum. It
was an ideal setting. It
was quiet, and Violet created just the right
mood for the minuet. Then the fire alarm
went off. People reacted quickly. Someone
called the firefighters and someone dialed
the police.

Noel
So why was
it chaotic?

Diana

Some people reacted badly. They created a fuss and started pushing and running as they tried to get out of the museum.

Noel

Where were you?

Diana

I was just inside the museum door. I had the video camera. I was videoing the performance for some clients from Iowa who sang the duet at the museum last week. I thought the video was going to get ruined.

Noel

Did you see the fire?

Diana

No. As soon as I saw that I couldn't influence what was going on, I called out to Violet to come with me until the chaos was over.

Noel

Well, at least you're both safe. We'd better go out and check the damage to the museum. The police might want to see your video.

Romeo and Juliet

Chloe, Theo

Theo

Let's go to the rodeo.

Chloe

I don't want to go to the rodeo. I want to get a video.

Theo

That's a good idea. We can get a video about rodeos.

Chloe

You know I dislike rodeos! I like science fiction, music, and history, but not rodeos.

Theo

And I suppose you want poetry, too.

Chloe

I really feel like getting one of those historical videos. The ones where people play violins, sing duets, and dance minuets.

Theo

OK. Let's get two videos. One about rodeos and one that's historical.

Chloe

That's a great idea. We could get *Romeo and Juliet*.

Theo

Romeo and Juliet? Who are Romeo and Juliet?

Chloe

Oh! You don't know anything about Romeo and Juliet?

Theo

I know a lot about science, diet, pioneers, lions
and rodeos. Just nothing about Romeo
and Juliet.

Chloe

Romeo and Juliet were in love a long time ago.
They were young, like us.

Theo

So what happened to them?

Chloe

Their families didn't want them to see each other. It was all so cruel. Their families created such a fuss, it all ended up in chaos. Romeo and Juliet both died.

Theo

Chaos! Sounds a bit gross to me! If that's historical, I'd rather watch a rodeo.

Chloe

Okay, I'll watch the rodeo video with you, if you'll watch the *Romeo and Juliet* video with me. Deal?

Theo

It's a deal. What if both videos are out?

Chloe

If they are, we'll have to watch that lion video again.